# NURSERY SONGS
## at the PIANO

### LEVEL 1

## arranged by JAMES BASTIEN

KJOS  NEIL A. KJOS MUSIC COMPANY • SAN DIEGO, CALIFORNIA

# PREFACE

The songs in this book are easily arranged for the young student to play, sing, and enjoy. **Nursery Songs at the Piano** may be used with Level 1 of **Bastien Piano Basics**, or with a first book of any piano course.

The pieces are arranged in a progressive order of difficulty.

We offer you our best wishes with these familiar songs.

Neil A. Kjos Music Company
James Bastien
Jane Smisor Bastien

# ABOUT THE ARRANGER

James Bastien has written a great deal of music for both children and adults. He graduated from Southern Methodist University where he studied with Gyorgy Sandor.

Mr. Bastien has been a faculty member at Notre Dame, Tulane, and Loyola Universities, and a summer faculty member at Tanglewood and the National Music Camp at Interlochen, Michigan.

He now resides in La Jolla, California, where he and his wife continue to write music of interest to piano students.

# CONTENTS

√  *

* To reinforce the feeling of achievement, the teacher or student may put a √ when the page has been mastered.

ISBN 0-8497-9345-9

# Hickory, Dickory, Dock

**Lively**

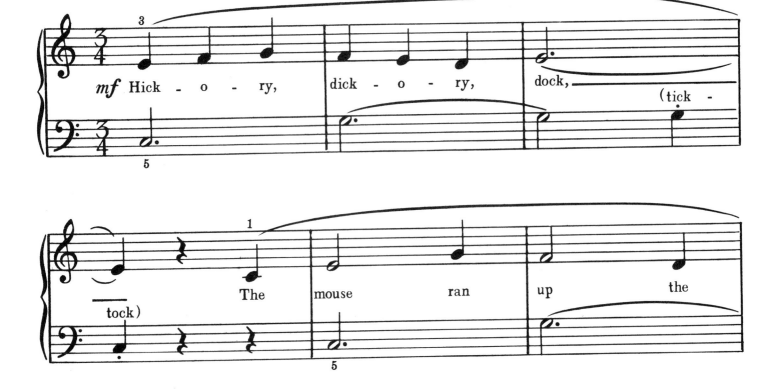

*mf* Hick - o - ry, dick - o - ry, dock, (tick -

tock) The mouse ran up the

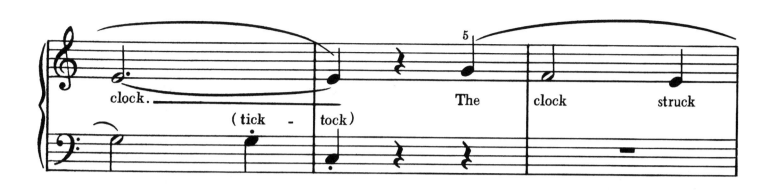

clock. _____ (tick - tock) The clock struck

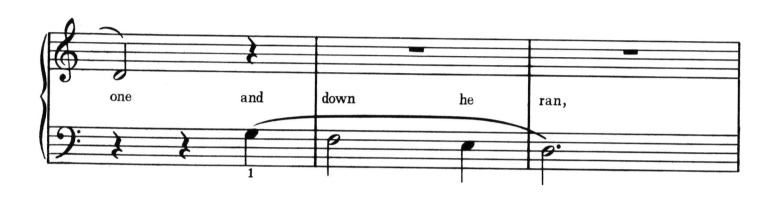

one and down he ran,

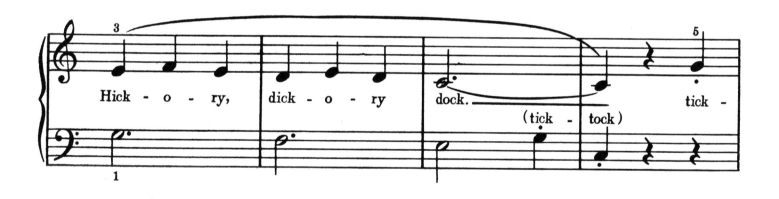

Hick - o - ry, dick - o - ry dock. _____ (tick - tock) tick -

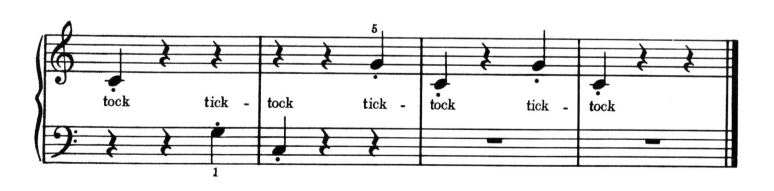

tock tick - tock tick - tock tick - tock

# Lazy Mary

**Moderato**

La - zy Mar - y will you get up, Will

you get up will you get up?

La - zy Mar - y will you get up? Will

**Play both hands one octave higher.**

you get up to - day?

No, no Moth - er I won't get up, I

won't get up, I won't get up!

No, no Moth - er I won't get up, I

won't get up to day!

8

# Hey, Diddle Diddle 3-14-94

**Moderato**

WP242

# Little Dog Gone

**Moderato**

# Pop! Goes the Weasel

**Lively**

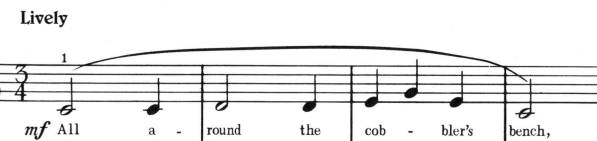

All a - round the cob - bler's bench, the

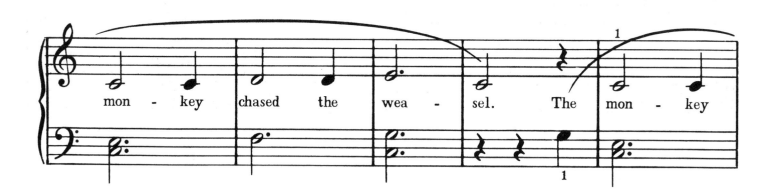

mon - key chased the wea - sel. The mon - key

thought 'twas all in fun. Pop! goes the

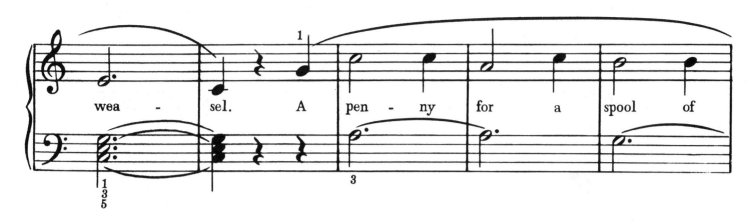

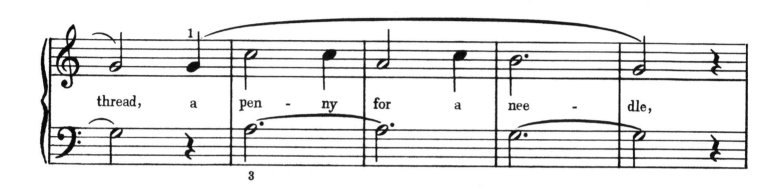

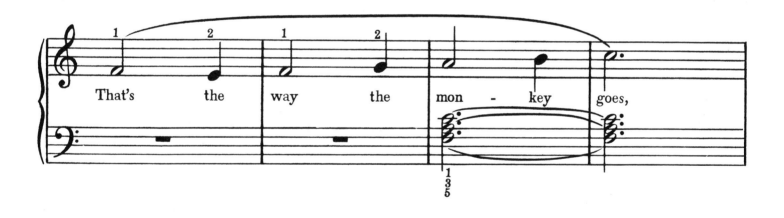

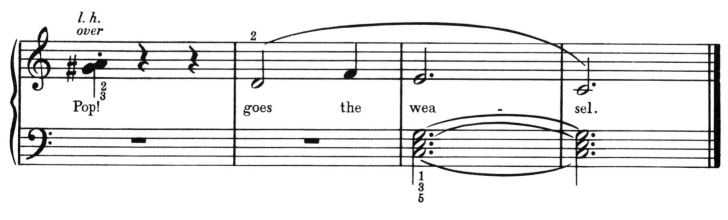

# Old MacDonald

5-2-94

**Moderato**

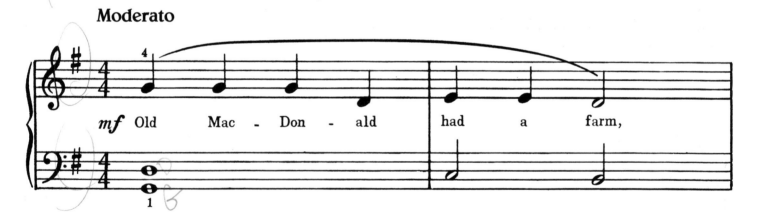

*mf* Old Mac - Don - ald    had    a    farm,

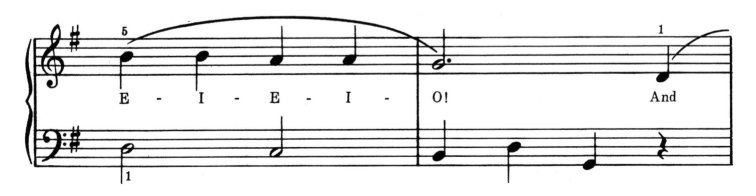

E - I - E - I - O!                    And

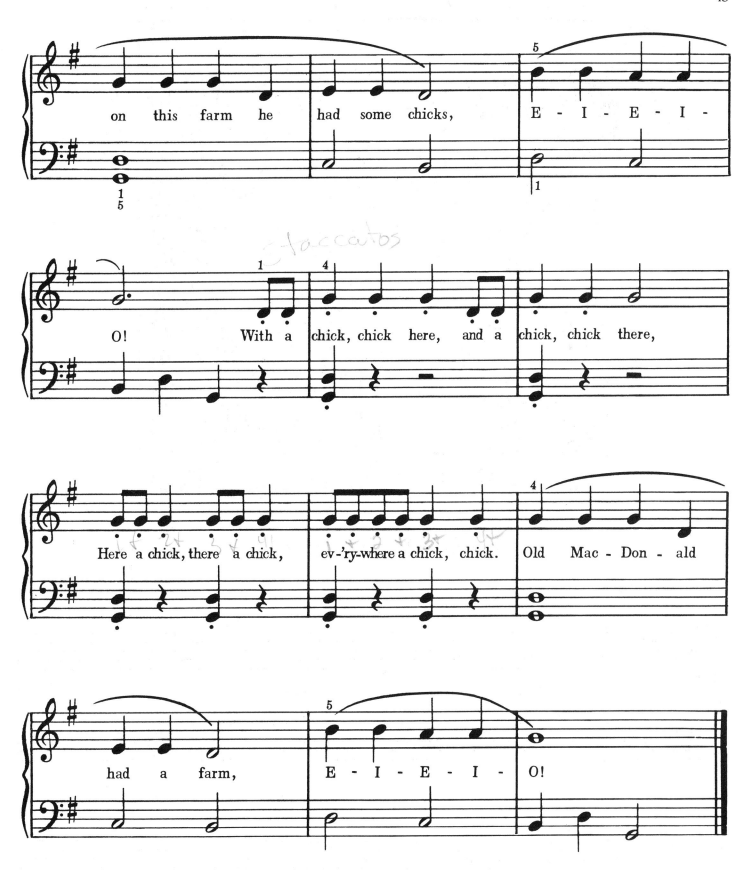

This song may be played with other animal names:

Cows.... moo, moo          Cats.... meow, meow
Sheep.... baa, baa          Dogs.... bow bow
Ducks.... quack, quack      Geese.... honk, honk

# This Old Man

*4-25-94*

**Lively**

*mf* 1. This old man, he played one, He played nick - nack

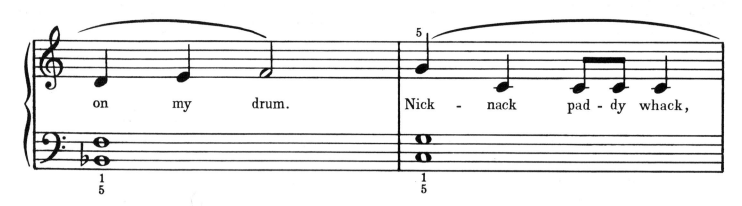

on my drum. Nick - nack pad - dy whack,

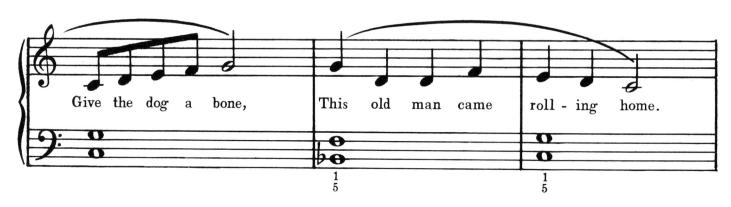

Give the dog a bone, This old man came roll - ing home.

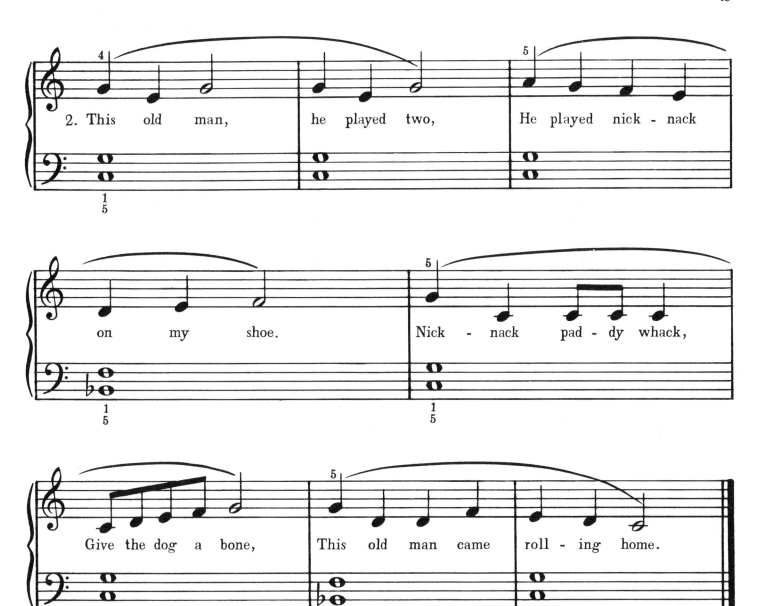

3. This old man, he played three,
He played nick-nack on my knee.

4. This old man, he played four,
He played nick-nack on my door.

5. This old man, he played five,
He played nick-nack on my hive.

6. This old man, he played six,
He played nick-nack on my sticks.

7. This old man, he played seven,
He played nick-nack up to Heaven.

8. This old man, he played eight,
He played nick-nack on my gate.

9. This old man, he played nine,
He played nick-nack on my line.

10. This old man, he played ten,
He played nick-nack over again.

# Old Woman In the Shoe

**Sadly**

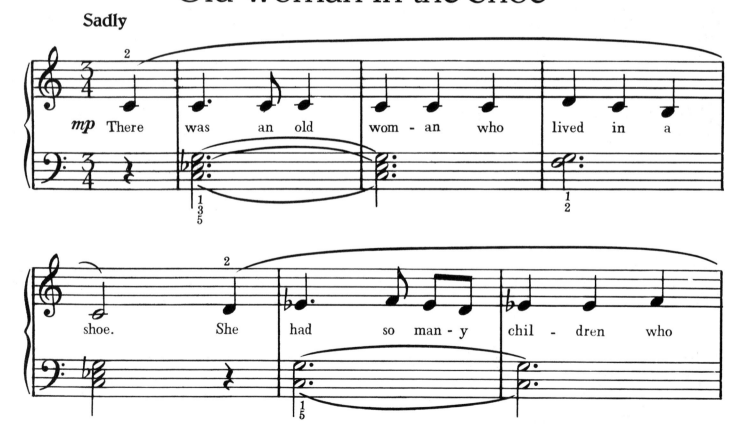

*mp* There was an old wom - an who lived in a

shoe. She had so man - y chil - dren who

al-ways cried "boo - hoo!" So she gave them some

broth with - out an - y bread, And

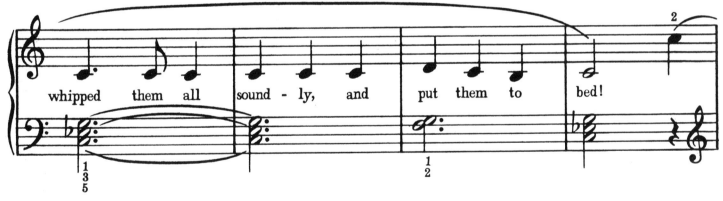

whipped them all sound - ly, and put them to bed!

*rit.*

# Eency Weency Spider

**Lively**

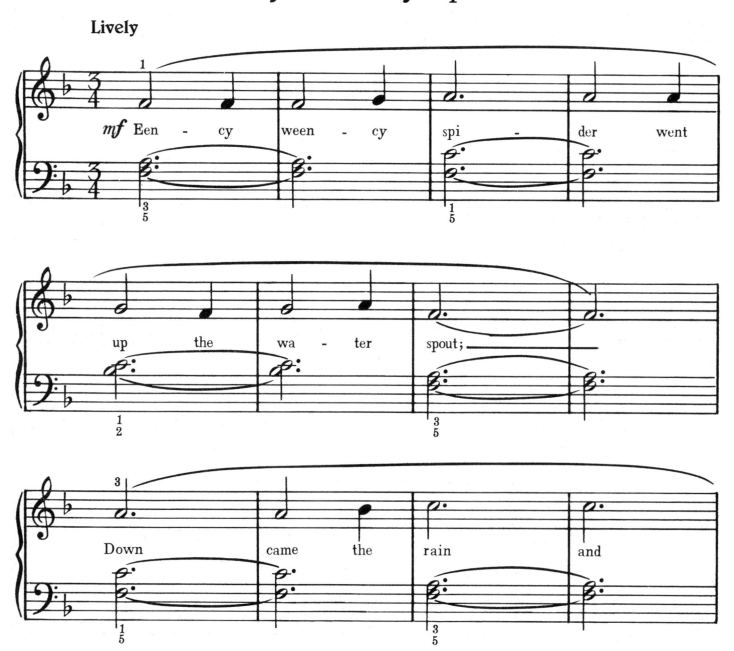

Een - cy ween - cy spi - der went

up the wa - ter spout;

Down came the rain and

washed the spi - der out.

Out came the sun and

dried up all the rain, And the

een - cy ween - cy spi - der went

up the spout a - gain!

# Peter, Peter

**Brightly**

*Observe the L.H. changes of position in this piece.

pump - kin    shell    and    there    he    kept    her

ver - y    well.    *f* Pe - ter    was    a    mer - ry    lad, he

got    his    fea - tures    from    his    Dad, but    his    poor    wife    she

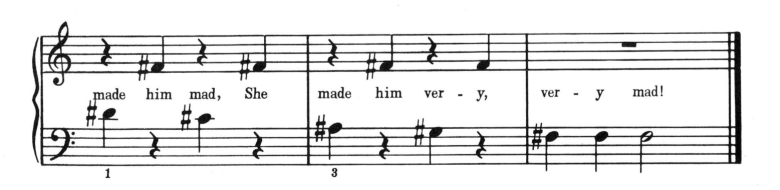

made    him    mad,    She    made    him    ver - y,    ver - y    mad!

# Old Mother Hubbard

**Slowly**

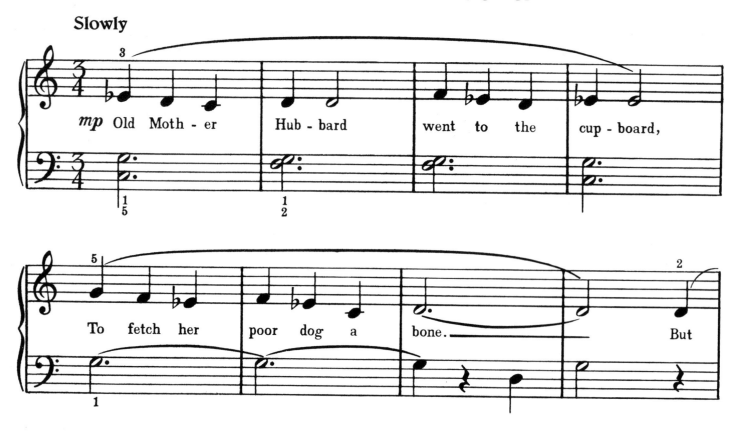

Old Moth - er Hub - bard went to the cup - board,

To fetch her poor dog a bone. But

# Little Boy Blue

**Moderato**